MUPPET TREASURE TREASURE HUNT

By Lara Bergen

Illustrated by Joe Ewers

MUPPET PRESS

MAMMOTH • LONDON

First published in Great Britain in 1996 by Mammoth, an imprint of Reed Children's Books
Michelin House, 81 Fulham Road, London SW3 6RB, and Auckland, Melbourne, Singapore and Toronto
Illustrated by Joe Ewers. Cover design by Graphiti Design & Production.

ISBN 0 7497 2785 3
Printed in Great Britain
Jewel stickers manufactured in China

If it's fortune you seek, then it's
your lucky day.
For behold! Here's a map that will
show you the way
To an island where treasure
is buried, it's told—
On the way you'll find pirates,
adventure, and gold!

Hidden away on each page of this book
Is one special treasure—you just have to look.
Use the riddles to help you, but please don't stop there.
More hidden surprises appear everywhere!

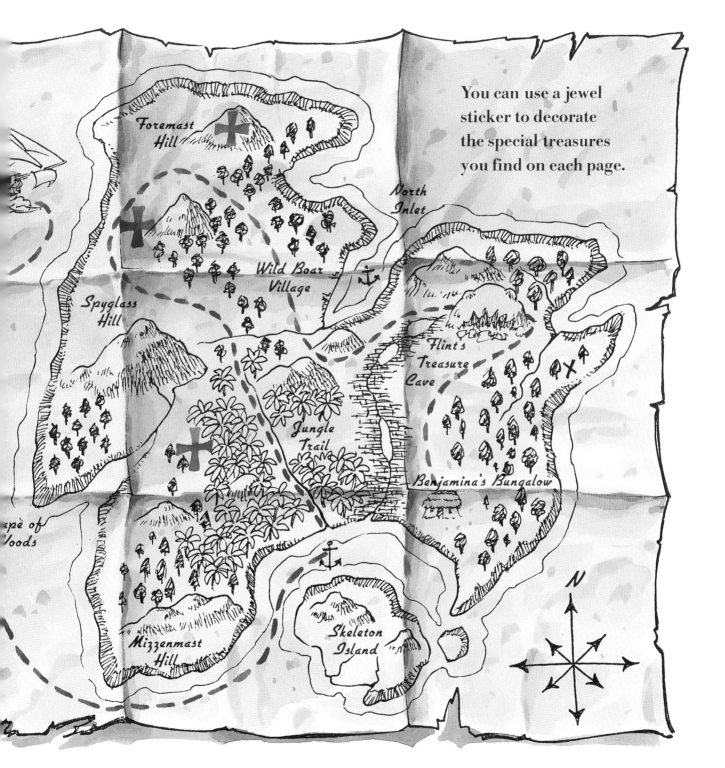

You can use a jewel sticker to decorate the special treasures you find on each page.

Foremast Hill

North Inlet

Spyglass Hill

Wild Boar Village

Flint's Treasure Cave

Jungle Trail

Benjamina's Bungalow

Cape of Woods

Mizzenmast Hill

Skeleton Island

N

Welcome, me mateys, to ye Olde Benbow Inn,
A jolly good place for a hunt to begin.
First find the **goblet**, and then make a toast.
(But watch out for the black spot
   and Captain Flint's ghost!)

See if you can also find: Billy Bones's dirty sock; Scooter's skateboard; Camilla the Chicken; a smiley face merit badge.

Our next stop is down at the Squire's
  royal manse,
Where more treasure awaits if you just
  take a chance.
The Squire will not only supply you a ship,
He's hidden a **platter** to take on your trip!

See if you can also find:
Beaker's old sneaker;
funny nose glasses;
a propeller beanie;
a bunch of bananas.

Down at the harbor, your ship waits for you.
But—*shiver me timbers!*—what a strange-looking crew!
It's lucky for you that somewhere in this scene
Is a **sword** just in case any sailors get mean.

See if you can also find: Clueless Morgan's false teeth; a ship in a bottle; a sneaky old snake; Captain Flint's skull and bones.

To make sure that your map stays as safe
      as can be,
Captain Smollett will keep it while you
      are at sea.
Hidden as well from the rough crew above
Is a lovely **framed picture** of Smollett's
      true love.

See if you can also find: Captain Smollett's teddy bear; Mr. Arrow's bowling ball; a pepperoni pizza; a high-heeled shoe.

Ahoy there, matey! Now it's time to set sail.
You're bound for adventure. (Let's hope you don't fail!)
For many a treasure's been buried at sea. . . .
In fact, there's a **chest** here, but where could it be?

See if you can also find: a rubber ducky; a submarine sandwich; a can of sardines; a kiddy swimming tube.

Land ho! Treasure Island appears up ahead.
Many have sailed here . . . though most are
   now dead!
But rather than worry 'bout that kind of thing,
Try finding a **crown** that is fit for a king.

See if you can also find: Blind Pew's sunglasses; suntan lotion; a sand castle; a beach umbrella.

Let's follow the trail to the skeleton tree—
Ten paces, turn left, and then count to three.
Now find a **bracelet**—or see if you can.
But also beware of the one-legged man!

See if you can also find: Long John's long johns;
a baby bottle; a telescope; a telephone.

Thanks to a detour, you meet the Boar Queen.
(The *piggiest* goddess that you've ever seen.)
"Boom-sha-ka-sha-ka-sha-ka!" the boars shout.
The Queen's lost her **scepter**. Can you help her out?

See if you can also find: a boar's surfboard; the
Swedish Chef's hat; a boom box; a box of popcorn.

You found old Flint's treasure cave just like a pro.
But the chests are all empty! Where *did* the loot go?
It looks as if someone has taken your share.
But perhaps there's one **jewelry box** hidden somewhere. . . .

See if you can also find:
a piggy bank; a "skeleton"
key; a three-dollar bill; an
extra-lucky five-leaf clover.

What's this? It's the treasure! And wouldn't you know!
You'd find it all here in the Queen's bungalow!
With all of that treasure you found on your way—
It looks like it really *is* your lucky day!

See if you can also find: Miss Piggy's barbell; her fluffy French poodle; her hair dryer; her favorite perfume.

THE END!